ANTARCTICA

Voices from the Silent Continent

COMPILED BY GABRIELLE MASON PEARSON

EDITED BY RICHARD ADAMS

The

Montagne Jeunesse

ANTARCTICA APPEAL

 Headway · Hodder & Stoughton

British Library Cataloguing in Publication Data

Cataloguing in Publication Data has been recorded at the British Library

ISBN 0 340 542551

First published 1990

© 1990 Montagne Jeunesse

Typeset by Rowland Phototypesetting Limited, Bury St Edmunds, Suffolk Printed in Great Britain for the educational publishing division of Hodder and Stoughton Limited, Mill Road, Dunton Green, Sevenoaks, Kent by Cambus Litho, East Kilbride

FOREWORD
ROBERT SWAN
Polar Explorer and Environmentalist

In 1983 I went to Sir Peter Scott to ask him to be the patron of my expedition which was to follow in the footsteps of his father, to the South Pole.

Not only did he kindly agree, he fired my imagination with his descriptions of the beauty of Antarctica and his passion that it should be preserved as an unexploited wilderness.

I pledged to him and to the public that my expedition would not leave any evidence of its presence on the continent. It was to be a difficult and expensive pledge to keep, but it was the beginning of my commitment to awakening the public's mind to the importance of Antarctica, both ecologically and as a unique example of a continent that is not owned by anyone.

The purity and mystery of Antarctica cast a particular spell over me during the 8 months of winter prior to the start of our walk. We had become familiar, even friendly with the native penguin and seal colonies. Three of our team had spent several weeks looking for the Emperor Penguin rookery at Cape Crozier. We had marvelled at the Arctic tern's arrival in Antarctica to avoid the Arctic winter.

Witnessing these creatures struggle for survival in such inhospitable surroundings helped to forge my conviction that Antarctica should not be exploited for minerals and oil.

Mr Joe Farmen of the British Antarctic Survey has shocked the world with his revelation on the hole of the ozone layer over the Antarctic. Not only is Antarctica at risk on the ground but also from atmospheric pollution created by those very nations lusting for its wealth beneath the ice.

Morally how can several wealthy nations exploit and threaten the last wilderness on earth?

Antarctica should remain a pristine platform for science. Now that Sir Peter Scott has died we should all take on the responsibility of being the caretakers of this precious continent.

Actions speak louder than words.

CONTENTS

1

INTRODUCTION

Antarctica –
Voices from the
Silent Continent

GREGORY BUTCHER

There is so much yet to learn about Antarctica – but we will never satisfy our need to know if we help to destroy it.

PATRICK ALLEN
Actor

Antarctica is the world's last pristine wilderness, but its future is under threat, and with it the natural habitat of millions of birds, marine mammals and ocean life. During the next few months, the Antarctic Treaty nations of the world will be deciding what the future of Antarctica is to be: whether to protect or plunder the finite resources – oil, gas and valuable minerals – which lie hidden beneath the ice cap.

Barry Fantoni

Why are we all dressed up? I'll tell you why we are all dressed up: We're attending the first night of the destruction of the Antarctic, that's why we're all dressed up

Platinum, uranium, coal, iron and other minerals are believed to be present on the continent, but the possibility of offshore oil reserves is attracting the greatest interest. The technology now exists to operate oil rigs in Antarctic seas, although such an operation would be fraught with danger.

The mining installations would all have to be on the narrow ice-free coastal areas, where the vast penguin and seal-breeding colonies are already in competition with scientific bases.

Antarctic seas have open water for only a few months of the year. Vast drifting icebergs and violent storms would make passage for oil tankers very dangerous.

Mountains of drifting ice dominate the bay

The *Exxon Valdez* disaster (off the coast of Alaska in 1989) demonstrated the devastating effect of an oil spill in a polar region. The spill saw 35,000 tonnes of oil spread over 4,800 square kilometres of water, and fouling 1,300 kilometres of shoreline. Hundreds of thousands of marine and terrestrial animals were killed. By mid-September, 1989, over 34,000 sea birds, nearly 10,000 sea otters, 147 sea eagles and at least 9, but possibly as many as 16, whales had been counted as victims of the oil. Huge stretches of Alaskan coastline remain oiled today. The long term ecological impact still remains to be seen.

Antarctica is waiting for the world to decide its fate. Once the wilderness quality is lost, it can never be recovered. Scientists already know that world pollutants have reached Antarctica, as it was here that the 'hole' in the ozone layer was first

We look on at the natural and man-made disasters of the world, and grieve for the death and damage they cause. Antarctica is a continent which can be protected from man-made disaster if only we can see the benefit before it is too late.

RICHARD O'SULLIVAN
Actor

discovered. Antarctica is therefore a valuable scientific base from which to measure pollution in the rest of the world. The protection of the Antarctic ice cap itself is vital, as it plays a key role in regulating the Earth's climate and sea levels. The sterilisation of the Antarctic ocean by pollutants, which would kill the krill, on which everything from whales downwards feeds, would be a very grave disaster.

A glimpse of the majestic beauty of Antarctica

The Antarctic ice sheet is a history book, revealing climatic and atmospheric changes in the earth's development. Samples taken by drilling into the ice have provided information on past ice ages, sea levels and solar activity. In the absence of local pollutants, it is possible to measure the world-wide spread of industrial pollution: pesticides have been found in Antarctic air and ice. This kind of research depends on a pristine environment and will become impossible once minerals exploitation begins.

Without the Antarctic wilderness, the fight for planet Earth is lost.

DAVID BELLAMY
Naturalist

Let me quote from a letter I received at the end of October 1989, from a British scientist on board a ship in the Antarctic Ocean: he wrote, 'In the Polar Regions today, we are seeing what may be early signs of man-induced climatic change. Data coming in from Halley Bay and from instruments aboard the ship on which I am sailing show that we are entering a Spring Ozone depletion which is as deep as, if not deeper, than the depletion in the worst year to date. It completely reverses the recovery observed in 1988. The lowest recording aboard this ship is only 150 Dobson units for Ozone total content during September, compared with 300 for the same season in a normal year.' That, of course, is a very severe depletion.

He also reports on a significant thinning of the sea ice. He writes that, in the Antarctic, 'Our data confirms that the first-year ice, which forms the bulk of the sea ice cover, is remarkably thin and so is probably unable to sustain significant atmospheric warming without melting. Sea ice,' he continues, 'separates the ocean from the atmosphere over an area of more than 30 million square kilometres. It reflects most of the solar radiation falling on it, thus helping to cool the earth's surface. If this area were reduced, the warming of earth would be accelerated due to the extra absorption of radiation by the ocean.'

'The lesson of these Polar processes,' he goes on, 'is that an environmental or climatic change produced by man may take on a self-sustaining or "runaway" quality . . . and may be irreversible.' That is from the scientists who are doing work on the ship that is presently considering these matters.

These are sobering indications of what may happen and they led my correspondent to put forward the interesting idea of a World Polar Watch, amongst other initiatives, which will observe the world's climate system and allow us to understand how it works.

MARGARET THATCHER
Prime Minister

The effects of global warming, atmospheric pollution and a seriously disintegrating ozone layer can be measured only in near pristine conditions in Antarctica. To act wisely in the light of the results of such research is far more important than the mining of a finite quantity of fossil fuels. Such mining can only intensify global warming.

The world must decide which is more important: the protection of Antarctica as a World Park – or its exploitation as a site for mining.

2

JOURNEY
SOUTH

An Ornithologist's

Voyage

KEITH SHACKLETON

Just about the only place left in the world not touched by mankind. Wildlife doesn't just live there – wildlife owns it. Surely the pollution crime can be averted.

JOHN LESLIE
Radio Personality

There is a welcome law of nature that smooths the paths of 'ornithologists' like me. It may also have played a significant part in shaping my passion for high latitudes, north and south, in general and in particular, the wildlife that belongs there.

The law, roughly outlined, proclaims that the further one gets from the Equator, the fewer the species, and therefore the lower the confusion factor for someone like me when it comes to identification. It is very simple.

By species I mean everything: birds, mammals, reptiles, insects, plants – everything that lives. Someone once told me there were nearly a quarter of a million different insects and spiders in the Amazon Basin alone, of which less than one third have been scientifically described. There are 100,000 plants, 2,000 known fishes and 1,700 birds – one fifth of the checklist for this whole planet. It is small wonder that I plied around this area in my working days there in a state of permanent mental seize-up. To be blinded by colours and markings is all excitement; it is the confusion that saddens.

But move away from the tropics with their intricate, arcane and often minute ecosystems, which flourish in the damp heat and things begin to change. By the 40s and 50s of latitude, north and south, the picture is beginning to look a lot less daunting. (The ability to recognise every British breeding species is no uncommon feat for the average birdwatcher, though some of the vagrants can still be perplexing.) Get into the 60s and finally the 70s and the exercise begins to freewheel gently downhill. Though populations may run into millions of individuals, their actual species can be totted up on fingers.

These are the hardened, perfected, indomitable forms that have filtered through the evolutionary process. They are the ones designed to live and move and have their being in the harshest environments of all, and they look the part.

Frigate birds hanging on the wind over the harbour at Rio and jewel-like, scissor-tailed hummingbirds taking midges on the hover over dockside shrubs are the last reminders of the tropics. With the gentle lift of the seas on a southerly course and the last of the flying fish skipping away from the bow-wave, there is soon the feel of the South Atlantic.

It is early December. Great shearwaters are around, completing their yearly ocean circuit. These are birds that have passed Britain, moved on through the North Atlantic, spent the late summer days skimming the Davis Strait. They will have seen the massive Greenland icebergs in Melville Bay and the pack off Baffin Island. They have sped like little shadows in and out of the fog veils over the Grand Banks, passed Hatteras into the Gulf Stream, and on southward. Now in the late Austral spring, they are on their way to Tristan da Cunha to breed and a few to the Falkland Islands.

The Falklands, to a south-bound birder, is the last place that looks a bit like home. Here are a handful of real 'LBJs', (little brown jobs!) the occasional storm-driven landbird from continental South America, a collection of vagrants that more than double the breeding total of some 60 species. The land has the look of the Hebrides: racing clouds on a boisterous wind, sharp showers and idyllic sparkling clearances over an ochre landscape. Grey rock buttresses thrust through the generous sweeping lines of weather-moulded uplands. Everywhere the sea; rafts of kelp and pristine beaches. There is no view on the Falklands without its counterpart somewhere in the Northern or the Western Isles or across in Connemara.

Is it really worth destroying such beauty in the name of progress?

GEORGE MEDLEY
Director Worldwide Fund for Nature

Nesting black-browed albatross and rockhopper penguins

Let's not allow our greed,
stupidity and lack of foresight
to spoil Antarctica.

JOSS ACKLAND
Actor

The weather too is warm, or at least what is euphemistically called 'parka warm'. Sir Ernest Shackleton's comment that he had never been so cold in all his life as he was in the guest room at Government House, Port Stanley, has to be taken in the spirit of the moment. The stabilising effect of the southern ocean keeps winter averages surprisingly close to the mean temperatures of summer. Of course, it can be cold, but there are many shirt-sleeve days. One I shall always remember was spent watching Des and Jen Bartlett film a peregrine eyrie. We sat on the clifftop rocks, shirtless in blazing sunshine. The sea below was wrinkled by a balmy breeze and blue as the Mediterranean. Little rusty butterflies – the endemic Falkland fritillaries – jigged along close to the turf, as if fearful that a change in the weather could blow them away from their islands forever.

The Falklands are a paradise for botanists too. The same natural law applies – luxuriant growth but fewer species. Moreover another law manifests itself here. The nearer one gets to the Poles, the closer to sea level can be found what we think of in milder latitudes as traditional alpine plants. On Mount Kenya, for instance, one would need to climb almost to the snow line to find the type of vegetation which, in the Falklands, thrives just a few feet above the maritime splash-zone. The springy upland turf and hill bog that inspired the word 'yomping' is as lovely a surface to walk over as exists on earth.

Gorse in full bloom on the Falkland Islands

Over 250 plants flourish here, of which 163 are native species. Many are familiar old friends with essentially English connotations: buttercups and clover, daisies and dandelions, and all growing – just as they do in Tierra del Fuego – larger, taller and sweeter scented than they do at home. Sickening, isn't it?

Gorse is a prime example. Brought in by settlers from Scotland for hedging and windbreaks, it flowers so densely in November and December that some bushes are literally all flowers and scarcely a green prickle can be seen. But when the flowers go, they go without trace. The old Scots saying 'when you can find no flower upon the gorse, love is out of season' would indeed cast a dread shadow for a good ten months of the year if applied to the Falklands.

The most striking difference lies with the wildlife. September sees the elephant-seals hauled out and the ponderous, vociferous rut beginning. Big bulls are shaping up to rivals all along the beach: arched up like giant maggots, inflated noses wobbling, vying with one another for the few extra inches of height which proclaim supremacy.

Young elephant seals basking on the shoreline

We've ruined our part of the world, please don't do the same to Antarctica.

BERYL REID
Actress

Fur seals and southern sea lions are ashore, too, and the penguins are coming in. By Christmas, penguin rookeries are in full swing. Hardy, seemingly indestructible little rockhoppers are bouncing in from the sea, tumbling over the rocks, assembling miraculously for a moment only for the slate to be swept clean by another thunderous wave. Then back they come and keep on coming until finally they make it. Hopping double-footed in bouncing ranks, they mount the cliffs, 200 feet (60m) or more, to nest beside the lordly black-browed albatrosses: the masters of soaring flight and the flightless within bill-touching distance of one another and in perfect harmony.

Family parties of steamer ducks, kelp geese and crested ducks swim offshore with their rapidly growing young, coaxing little, fluffy flotillas through fronds of weed. The opportunists are about too. Brown skuas and 'Johnny rooks' – the striated caracara – have their eyes on the main seasonal chance – unguarded eggs, lost chicks and storm-injured adults. Johnny rook is the joke bird of the islands. Stories both true and apocryphal abound and all concern its fascination for assorted human artefacts and its reactions to them. In appearance it is somewhere between a crow and a mini-vulture, smartly striped as the name implies and with the hoppity truculent gait of an investigating magpie. Nothing could give it more delight than coming upon an unattended rucksack – especially one with zip pockets.

Johnny rook will unzip and zip up each pocket in turn, seeming to savour the rasping sound so close to its ear. But should it find goodies inside the pocket, there is no end to the possibilities. Films, a bar of chocolate, string, gloves, hip flask, penknife, compass. All will be taken out, examined, turned over, picked up, dropped and even kicked. Once I watched powerless as a Johnny rook removed a pair of binoculars, examined them critically and dragged them a short distance over the rocks by the strap before it took off with an air of derision and dropped them into the sea!

This tameness in animals begins here and carries right through to the Antarctic; the tameness of unfamiliarity with man and the greatest compliment that man could be paid. It is something more than a simple tolerance of close approach, rather an impulse to make the play, to come and meet you, either out of curiosity, the hope of gain perhaps, or some indefinable urge for companionship. The tussock bird will come to a stranger's hand for crumbs of bread. The nesting albatross will lean over as if to check the progress of a sketch,

Let us pray that common sense and selflessness will prevail long enough to protect this fragile environment from wanton destruction by thoughtless and greedy men.

JOHN BLASHFORD-SNELL
Director General, Operation Raleigh

A nesting wandering albatross, South Georgia. These birds have a wing span of 11 feet

responding with interest to the sound of pencil tip on paper. The young elephant seal will writhe in ecstasy when scratched, and fat little Commerson's dolphins swim between sea-booted legs, escort the boat and all but run themselves aground in their impulse to communicate and join the party. The more the applause, the more they love it, and with their unique communication system, they seem to send for their friends to come and join in.

Every major group of birds on the British list is represented in the Falklands except for the gamebirds and the alcids, whose niche in the islands is filled by five species of penguin and two diving petrels. To press on south from Port Stanley is to leave the last of this essential Britishness in the bird field – and others as well. By the time South Georgia is reached, a voyage of 750 miles, an altogether different picture is waiting, with the demure little local pipit the last indigenous landbird, the last true LBJ before the Great White South.

Ruins of the whaling station at Grytviken, South Georgia

South Georgia, although a good deal further east, lies only two degrees south of the Falklands. One could be excused, therefore, for expecting a similar aspect and climate to match. But the truth is very different. The rounded, peaty Western Isles look exists only in very isolated and restricted places and at lower levels: the flavour of the island as a whole is pure Antarctica. Peaks 9,000 feet (2,743m) high thrust into the clouds and snow fields, great glaciers and rock faces are the backbone of a beautifully forbidding island some 90 miles (144km) long, lying like a monstrous, frozen crescent across the west wind drift in the 50's of south latitutde. Height is not the only reason for the snowy aspect and the harsh climate: much has to do with the Antarctic Convergence.

Cold, north-going waters that surround the continent of Antarctica meet at a point where they sink below the warmer layers of surrounding ocean. At this point, heading south, the water temperature drops several degrees in a few miles. Sedimental nutrients from warmer seas well up and nourish the surface phytoplankton. The seas are enriched and teem with life, a glimpse of the very beginning of a short but virile and finely-balanced food chain which, with only a few links, connects single-celled drifting plants to the largest animals that ever inhabited the earth.

The circumpolar position of the Convergence is surprisingly constant and is marked on most charts. It passes to the south of the Falklands but sweeps north of South Georgia. In true geographic terms, the Convergence is the actual threshold of Antarctica, and by such reasoning South Georgia, lying within its cold embrace, is properly an Antarctic island. And yet here a pipit still sings, though it sings alone.

More human feet have trod this island than any other in the sub-Antarctic. It began when Captain James Cook's party from *Resolution* fired a 'discharge of small arms' to mark its formal possession in the name of King George on 17 January, 1775. In the early 1800s, sealers of many nations plundered here, and soon the fur seal population was all but gone. Whalers followed. The beginning of this century saw the first of the big land-based whaling stations. They were industrial townships, some with churches, even cinemas. There were six of them in all, employing caretaker trades all the year round, with an influx of thousands in the southern summer. When whaling was at its peak, 32 catchers operated out of South Georgia and over 7,000 whales might be killed in a single summer season.

Then in the early 1960s it all came to an end, more, it has to be said, through considerations of economics than conscience. Today the stations are in ruins, hovering in that limbo area that to some is unsightly litter, to others industrial archaeology. Elephant seals and fur seals doze indolently on the slip-ways and flensing plan. Machinery and buildings lie rusted and silent.

Throughout the island's 200 years of human history, exploration ships have visited, re-fuelled, taken on stores and rested in what Shackleton termed 'the gateway to Antarctica'. Bellingshausen was here in the *Vostok* and *Mirny* during his survey of the South Sandwich Islands, Weddell, Bransfield and Biscoe. Nordenskjold was here in the *Antarctic*: Scott in the *Discovery* and *Terra Nova*. Shackleton came in the *Endurance*, and finally the *Quest*, to die in Grytviken harbour and to be buried in the whalers' cemetery. Hardly a ship of note bound for the peninsular side of Antarctica failed to visit this island, which is probably quieter now than it has been for a century.

South Georgia: The grave of Sir Ernest Shackleton (Keith Shackleton Left and Capt. Hasse Nilsson – Master of M.V. 'Lindblad Explorer')

Despite the continued encroachment of mankind upon previously unspoilt areas of our planet, there are still sufficient natural resources to make the destruction of Antarctica unnecessary.

FATIMA WHITBREAD
Sports Personality

The same, however, cannot be said for the wildlife, and of these the most sensational comeback has been staged by the Kerguelan fur seal. During the summer rut they are ashore in numbers that must have compared with the spectacle that greeted Cook when he first sailed into Possession Bay. In their breeding free-for-all, albatross colonies – grey-headed in particular – are driven to higher ground, their favourite tussock areas flattened by the raucous mob of pinnepeds.

A handful of reindeer introduced by Norwegian whalers before the First World War have been a constant food source ever since and now stand at about 2,000 in three distinct herds – again looking bigger and better than their relations back in Norway. Elephant seals, once hunted hard for oil, are on the ascendant too, and provide a note of timeless repose, stretched out on the beaches and among the tussocks in somnolent contrast to the active, aggressive and surprisingly athletic fur seals. Sadly, it is only the whales that have not returned. They are still a rare sight, even the smaller species, whereas but a few decades ago fin and blue whales were shot by the score in Cumberland Bay itself.

One legacy of the whaling days lingers on in the empty buildings in the shape of rats and, as might be expected, they are bigger and fitter. Rats the size of young rabbits thump about on the rotting floorboards of the hayloft in Grytviken, as if they were wearing climbing boots, their heavy tails rasping over the woodwork. Imported rats spell disaster to any island – with the small, underground-nesting petrels the first to be at risk. But birds of all kinds suffer, and while rats seem to stay mostly around the shelter of the ruins, it is little wonder that no rat has made a footing there.

In South Georgia, our law of 'the higher the latitude, the lower the species count', clicks up a further notch. We now have only 29 breeding bird species with about the same score of recorded vagrants. This time, all but the Antarctic pipit, the endemic South Georgia pintail and the yellow-billed teal are birds of the sea and without any question the most spectacular is *Apenodytes patagonicus*, the king penguin. Although not quite the size of the truly Antarctic emperor, it is over a yard (1m) high and makes up the shortfall in sheer displacement by its elegance, its poise and the long-flippered dignity of its walk.

Though large rookeries exist on Crozet and Kerguelain in the Indian Ocean, and Macquarie in the Pacific sector of the southern ocean, the South Georgia population is impressive. The main concentrations are to the east in Royal Bay and St

King penguins with 'oakham boys', Bay of Islands, South Georgia

Andrews Bay, with a third close to the Grace Glacier in the Bay of Isles to the northwest, and all carry upwards of 10,000 breeding pairs. Many smaller rookeries are dotted about here and there, so that there are few beaches which lack the classic spectacle of parties of king penguins, immensely self-important, standing about chatting like delegates at some great Austral synod. Among them will be all-but-fledged young, the 'oakum boys' as early sailors knew them. Oakum was stock-in-trade to a shipwright carpenter for caulking the seams of ship's boats, and the young penguins resembled nothing so much as a wad of familiar caulking fibre – in colour as much as texture. Indeed, the density of the young coat puts a good few inches on a penguin's diameter, making the adults look positively under-nourished beside their offspring. King penguins have a breeding cycle which is unusual, to say the least, resulting in a

There will come a time when we will stop and realise that we have nothing left. It will slowly dawn on us that in our haste to gain so much, we are actually left with nothing.

GLORIA HUNNIFORD
TV and Radio Personality

normal pair producing two 'oakum boys' in a three-year period.

Across the bay a similar cycle is acted out with the great wandering albatross, resulting in a single young bird every alternate year. At the risk of appearing over-imaginative, I believe that the albatross's lifestyle is clearly written in its eye. No bird I know exhibits such an air of serene composure, of timeless content. Even in the passion of courtship composure prevails. Whilst tossing the head, clacking the bill, extending a magnificent 11 feet (3½m) of wingspread and prancing about in unashamed self-advertisement, there is no significant change in the eye, beyond perhaps a hint of amusement. Then the bird will utter its triumphant fanfare (likened by Niall Rankin to 'a man with a cleft palate endeavouring to reason with a restive horse') while the eye persists with its reflection of a deep inner peace.

The single egg is laid around Christmas-time but will not hatch until late March. A slow-growing chick, nourished at the price of far-flung ocean sorties, will not be fully fledged until the middle of the following summer. It will sit there, wearing its inherited composure like a warm eiderdown, through blizzards of winter that pile driven snow against its weather side, making the colony look like garden ornaments in a hard white Christmas. The following December it will be ready, with white head and patchy liver-brown plumage, to waddle splay-footed up to some point of vantage and from there lift off into the wind alone. Three hundred days on the nest have been crowned with success.

Just under 300 nautical miles east-south-east of South Georgia lies the northernmost island of the South Sandwich group – Zavodovoski. The Russian name, bestowed by Bellingshausen in 1819 during his survey, supersedes the group's collective title from James Cook's original discovery in 1775. Cook named them after Lord Sandwich, current First Lord of the Admiralty, a man ironically destined to achieve more lasting fame as the inventor of the original stopgap meal.

The island of Zavodovoski is unique – almost certainly the most unique of an already unique archipelago. Here is a fully active volcano, belching great cauliflowers of malodorous smoke and steam from its conical summit, 1,800 feet (550m) above sea level. Indeed, the aptly-named Mount Asphyxia is itself the island; the names are inseparable. The steeply-sloping upper levels are shifting, sliding banks of ash that deny any permanent footing. On the west side are precipitous cliffs, but down on the north and east-facing areas are gentler slopes that end at sea level with low, rocky buttresses and cinder beaches. This part is entirely given over to penguins. To all practical purposes, Zavodovoski is wall-to-wall penguins: chinstraps mostly and a few macaronis, carpeting the slopes like pepper and salt. An estimated 21 million nest here!

Lying to leeward, the air is filled with the sulphurous fumes of the mountain itself, but blended with the overtones of volcanically-toasted penguin guano and vomit on an industrial scale. One's ears are battered with the kind of clamour more akin to an aural affliction than an identifiable sound. And there is surely no other ornithological spectacle to match it – anywhere. Only 6°20′ further south, but 29°40′ further west, lies Prime Head, the extreme northern tip of the continent of Antarctica itself.

The peninsula of Graham Land, now called the Antarctic Peninsula in deference to the treaty, reaches like a long, crooked finger northwards, as if flicking the assorted islands of the South Shetlands group in the general direction of Cape Horn. It is by far the nearest point of the continent to the rest of the world. Its tip reaches as far north as a little over 63 south,

Lichens cover the rocks on which this banded brown skua rests. More than 350 lichens have been identified in the Antarctic

and not for nothing is it referred to as the 'banana belt' of the Antarctic. One can be much colder in Cambridge in January than on a summer's day here, but it is wise to remember that this fearsome and beautiful land always has another meteorological shot in its locker.

I will forbear to mention yet again all those fascinating statistics expressed by superlatives – the coldest, the highest, the windiest, the loneliest, etc. Antarctica is indeed all these things and many more, but most important, I feel, is that it is the last remaining true wilderness, its beauty that of intrinsic natural perfection.

> Antarctica is the last wilderness left on earth. It is virtually inaccessible and is the one remaining continent which is still exactly as it was created. Let's not allow our greed to spoil it.
>
> **FAITH BROWN**
> Comedienne

A gentoo penguin protects its young on the South Shetland Islands

I began with the law of declining species against increasing latitude. We are now down to 17 breeding birds, either on or in sight of Antarctica itself. There are so few that they can easily be listed: four penguins, seven petrels and storm petrels, one cormorant, two skuas, one gull, one tern and the inimitable and lovably ridiculous sheathbill – Antarctica's only answer to the Falklands' Johnny rook, and the only bird here without a webbed foot.

Though a fair crop of mosses, lichens and algae abound,

Drake Passage – 'First Ice'

there are only two vascular plants – *Deschampsia* and *Colobanthus* – both as diminutive and humble as a vascular plant can be. All other life on the land is microscopic.

But life exists in the sea in enormous abundance, nourishing the penguin hordes, the few remaining great whales and six species of seal. When it comes to the ocean, the equation of species against biomass is very striking. The commonest seal, for instance, is the crab-eater – curiously named, since there are no crabs for it to eat – which has an estimated population of about 30 million. There are actually more crab-eaters than the rest of the world's seals put together. It is the most numerous large carnivore on earth.

So the goal is reached. There is no need to look at, but none of it needs a field guide to name. Perhaps one of the greatest joys,

Antarctica is like a jewel, sparkling like snowflakes in the wintry sun. Let's nurture it and look after it: it belongs to nature and not to man.

ANDREW FORBES
Actor

Antarctica – why can't they just leave it alone? It is so beautiful and peaceful. It will never be ready for the intrusion of man, and will certainly never recover!

RICHARD BRIERS
Actor

especially for those who like to draw birds, is the opportunity to see species in bulk and thereby glean a wealth of attitude studies at every sitting. The backdrop has a beauty and grandeur that is devastating. There are no problems of approach; the subjects are both willing and infinitely drawable. Some are exceptional – Antarctica's blue-eyed shag must be the loveliest of all cormorants – but the one great star in the firmament will always be the snow petrel, sitting tight on her egg in a crevice; the whitest of plumage against lichen-encrusted rock, the clear, jet-black boot-button of an eye; the perfection of aerodynamic shape over the endless ice floes. This is the bird for me. Even more than a penguin, the snow petrel is the spirit of the white continent itself, the one that sticks pleasurably in the memory through northern summers and the siren that brings one irresistibly back.

Tabular iceberg in the Branfield Strait

The Antarctic Treaty

In 1991 the Antarctic Treaty, agreed by 16 nations, comes up for review. It grew from the goodwill of the International Geophysical Year, 1957 to 1958; came into being in 1959, and in essence is a blueprint for political and scientific harmony that could be a lesson for the world.

It covers Antarctica south of the sixtieth parallel, but sadly omits the Ocean. From it has grown a wealth of valuable concepts. The Scientific Committee on Antarctic research (SCAR) co-ordinates the scientific and logistical effects of the signatory nations, ensuring that data is shared and plans for future research made known to all members. It is hard to imagine a higher degree of international co-operation, its purpose the conservation of a very international heritage.

The year 1991 will be critical. The fervent optimist will always hope that a vote of 'no change', an endorsement of present policies (and extended to protect the ocean environment) will be the outcome. By the same token, the realist cannot help noticing signs of national chauvinism penetrating the scientific accord. One of the cornerstone articles of the treaty agrees to the shelving of prior territorial claims, yet these are still driven home by certain nations, kept alive and even developed. Another article forbids military activity except for the logistical support of scientists in the field. Yet barrack blocks are in places more noticeable than laboratories. Moreover, they tend to be used as a cynical means of proving 'settlement' and hence a device for bolstering a claim of sovereignty.

Anyone who truly loves this place recognises 'ownership' as preposterous. It is a world asset, a place of immeasurable value in its own right – provided the rapists can be held at bay.

Anyone who has studied the history of exploration knows the sacrifice, dedication and courage enshrined in Antarctica, and can take pride in his or her own country's enormous contribution. But that was the past. The future begins today. All that can be done is to urge every kind of diligence to ensure that this last inviolate land stays as it is, to exert its age-old influence on the weather patterns of our planet and to serve as a perpetual source of inspiration to the human spirit.

The governments of the world should think beyond commercial gain and remember that Antarctica belongs to the *world* and not to them.

BOB GELDOF
TV Personality,
Singer

3

A
CONTINENT
UNDER
SIEGE

GABRIELLE MASON
PEARSON

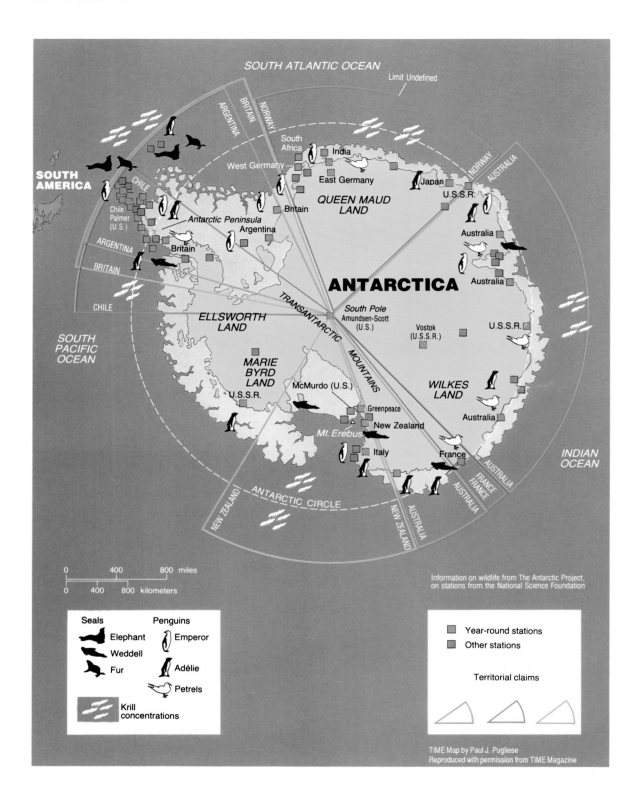

SOUTH ATLANTIC OCEAN

Limit Undefined

ARGENTINA
BRITAIN
NORWAY I

South Africa
India
West Germany
East Germany
Japan
U.S.S.R.
NORWAY
AUSTRALIA

SOUTH AMERICA

CHILE

Chile Palmer (U.S.)

Britain

QUEEN MAUD LAND

Antarctic Peninsula
Argentina

ARGENTINA

Britain

BRITAIN

ANTARCTICA

Australia

Australia

CHILE

ELLSWORTH LAND

South Pole
Amundsen-Scott (U.S.)

Vostok (U.S.S.R.)

U.S.S.R.

SOUTH PACIFIC OCEAN

TRANSANTARCTIC MOUNTAINS

MARIE BYRD LAND

U.S.S.R.

McMurdo (U.S.)

Greenpeace

New Zealand

Mt. Erebus

Italy

WILKES LAND

Australia

France

INDIAN OCEAN

AUSTRALIA
FRANCE
FRANCE
AUSTRALIA

NEW ZEALAND

ANTARCTIC CIRCLE

NEW ZEALAND

AUSTRALIA

0   400   800 miles
0   400   800 kilometers

Information on wildlife from The Antarctic Project, on stations from the National Science Foundation

Seals   Penguins
Elephant   Emperor
Weddell   Adélie
Fur   Petrels

Krill concentrations

Year-round stations
Other stations

Territorial claims

TIME Map by Paul J. Pugliese
Reproduced with permission from TIME Magazine

This is the coldest place on earth: the temperature can fall to minus 88°C, the ice can be up to two miles deep and the wind can blow at 200 miles an hour. And yet, despite all this, Antarctica is a place teeming with life.

Thousands of birds and mammals thrive in this vast winter wilderness. Antarctica is the world's largest continent. It is larger than Australia, more than half the size of the Soviet Union. It is 4½ million square miles of ice, covering 10% of the world's surface, containing 90% of the world's ice and 70% of its fresh water.

Graham Coast landscape, Antarctica

> Antarctica is like what life was like before the world began – the spaciousness, silence and sheer glory of an unadulterated world.
>
> **PETER HIRST-SMITH**
> Photographer of the Antarctic

Huge ice caves look inviting, yet can collapse at anytime, as the wind and ocean enter along lines of weakness

The area of the Antarctic ice-shelves has decreased by more than 750 square kilometres in the past ten years.

HON. FRANCIS MAUDE MP
Foreign Affairs Minister

As yet unspoilt, this great, frozen continent constitutes a yardstick against which the pollution of the rest of the world is measured. It has its own alarm system, too. As the planet becomes more and more polluted and global warming increases, the Antarctic ice will start to melt. If all the ice did melt, global sea level would rise by some 60 metres. The removal of the weight of ice would cause the rock surface to rise by 200–300 metres.

The Southern Ocean which surrounds Antarctica links the Atlantic, Pacific and Indian Oceans in a great expanse of circumpolar waters. With few surface obstacles, the waters are driven by the winds of the 'Roaring Forties', 'Furious Fifties', and 'Shrieking Sixties'. The ice cliffs and rocks of the Antarctic coastline are the boundary of the ravages of sea and wind currents.

The boundary of the Antarctic is hard to define, however, because the ice barrier fluctuates throughout the year. The sea around the coast freezes in winter, expanding to an area of around 20 million km². In summer, much of this melts to 3 million km², leaving vast icebergs that have broken from the ice shelves in the Ross and Weddell Seas to the north of the continent, and large expanses of solid pack ice. The boundary of Antarctica is generally considered to be an invisible frontier in the sea – the Antarctic Convergence Zone, where cold surface water from the continent reaches outwards to meet warmer surface waters from the Indian, Atlantic and Pacific Oceans.

Blue-eyed shags are frequent visitors

The atmosphere above the continent is thin and cloudless. Although exposed to long periods of sunshine, much of the heat from the sun is reflected off the ice. In 1985, scientists, studying the weather patterns and atmosphere over Antarctica, discovered a 'hole' in the ozone layer. This has been getting larger every spring. A depletion of ozone allows more of the sun's ultra-violet light to reach the earth's surface, causing damage to plants, an increase in skin cancers and ice to melt.

If the 'hole' continues to grow at its current rate, it is estimated that by the end of this century we will have lost one-third of our plant species. In Antarctica, this will mean a decline in the mass of phytoplankton. Phytoplankton, at the base of the food chain, sustains zooplankton, including krill, together with creatures higher up in the food chain: fish, squid, birds, seals and whales.

For 30 years the footprints of industrial and military mankind have been kept away from the continent by the Antarctic

Treaty, which has ensured that man's intrusion into Antarctica has so far been limited to a number of research stations. Member nations, however, including seven with territorial claims in the continent (Britain, Argentina, France, Norway, Australia, New Zealand and Chile), have adopted a Convention on Antarctic Mineral Resources which, if ratified, will permit commercial prospecting for the first time, thus paving the way for wholescale commercial exploitation of the continent.

Ninety per cent of the mainland is under ice almost a mile thick. Under the snow and ice of the Transantarctic Mountains lies what is possibly the world's greatest coal field, although its quality is thought to be poor. There is iron in the Prince Charles Mountains, and traces of other metals have been found on the continent, such as uranium, copper, chromium, zinc, silver, gold, manganese and titanium. Platinum deposits have been found in the Dufek Massif in considerable amounts. The temptation to exploit these minerals is obvious.

I endorse your concern for Antarctica.

Will our greed ever be satisfied? Can we not open up our narrow minds to see that by *not* mining Antarctica we will actually help ourselves more in the long run; and that by preserving this precious continent, our children will have a planet to live on?

RAY GALTON
Actor and Writer (by arrangement Tessa le Bars)

The rate of the ice movement depends upon a number of factors, including the size and thickness of the ice body

It's terribly important that everything in nature should be protected from pollution and the evils of industrialists and people who want to make money out of it.

JILLY COOPER
Authoress

If Antarctica is exploited for mineral resources and oil, it is estimated that its potential reserves will satisfy world demand for, at most, two years. Any accidental oil spillage, such as occurred recently when a tanker, attempting to avoid an iceberg, ran aground off the coast of Alaska, will take over five centuries to bio-degrade. The risks involved in shipping crude oil from the Antarctic across iceberg-laden seas, often subject to high winds, would be considerable. New species of animal life are still being discovered within the Antarctic and many of the intricacies of the region's ecological balance are yet to be fully understood.

An oil spill could spread over a vast area and affect everything in its path: wildlife, marine life, bird life and the very ice itself. Oil trapped in the ice would affect the most fundamental and essential part of the food chain, killing algae, plankton and krill – the staple diet of most other marine mammals, and the key to the entire Antarctic food chain. With a knock-on effect, every level of the food chain would suffer. This imposed imbalance of nature has been seen many times in other parts of the world. It is now threatening the last unspoilt place left on earth.

The implications of even limited exploitation of the Antarctic are difficult to gauge. Apart from the inevitable disturbance and destruction of wildlife, there would be irreparable damage to what is perhaps of the most value to us: the very ice itself. For, as well as being our yardstick for the present, the continent surrounding the South Pole is also an archive and a crystal ball rolled into one. Within its frozen strata lie the geological and atmospheric records of the planet dating back thousands of years, awaiting the keen eye of scientific man to read them and, with the knowledge they offer, perhaps see more clearly the possible dangers inherent in man's future development of the planet.

The first exploration of minerals is likely to take place in the ice-free regions, which represent 2% of the continent. These are the areas most heavily colonised by wildlife, and disturbance would have catastrophic effects on the natural habitat of seals, penguins, bird and plant life.

As well as the birds and sea mammals which inhabit Antarctica, there are interesting plant species. The snow and ice support snow algae, which tinge the surfaces yellow, green and reddish colours. The ice-free land supports a diversity of Antarctic lichen species, and in some coastal areas there are around 100 species of Antarctic mosses and liverworts, as well

If you saw Miss World this year, you will know we concentrated on the environment and green issues both in judges' questions and for the finalists on the stage. The contestants all gave very intelligent answers. It is amazing the way young people are becoming very much aware of the problem and will do all they can to help. Although I have never been to Antarctica, I sincerely hope that it will remain as unspoilt as nature intended.

ERIC MORLEY
Chairman, Miss World UK Ltd

Few flowering plants are able to survive in the Antarctic environment

as two species of higher plant, namely grass and the low-lying cushion plant. Living amongst this rather sparse vegetation are midges, mites and small flightless, primitive insects. In the sub-Antarctic region, which consists of various islands radiating outwards from the main continent, the vegetation is firmly established, supporting more species of insect.

The Antarctic environment is too delicate to accommodate human interference. A human footprint on a bed of lichen will take a decade to disappear because of the incredibly short growing season. Any disturbances to the frozen soil and rocks would create dust and debris, which accelerate the melting of snow and ice.

This cruel, hard, unforgiving continent offers a wealth of knowledge waiting to be discovered. The merest interference by man will decrease its scientific value beyond all measure and destroy the very records on which we rely. As Sir Peter Scott, the world-renowned artist and conservationist, wrote,

'The urge to find out more about remote parts of the earth drove my father to the Antarctic. That is very different from the urge to overcome technological challenges in

Can man truly justify this desecration of Antarctica as 'A step forward'? Surely, to have somewhere left which is natural is far better than a two-year supply of oil?

RUSTIE LEE
TV Personality

order to exploit all the earth's resources. I believe we should have the wisdom to know when to leave a place alone.'

As a continent, the Antarctic was first circumnavigated between 1772 and 1775 by James Cook. The abundant wildlife provided a hunters' paradise, and by the early 1900s both elephant and fur seals were nearly extinct. Over 1 million right, humpback, sei, sperm, blue, minke and fin whales were harpooned in Antarctic waters during this century, and the right, humpback, blue and fin whales are still on the endangered species list.

Exploration and discovery of the continent started in earnest in 1841 and in 1911 came the famous South Pole expeditions by Captain Robert Falcon Scott and by the Norwegian Amundsen. During the decades that followed, seven countries including the UK and Norway claimed territorial rights, while several others set up bases.

> For once there is still time to prevent a tragedy. We have seen what oil spills have done to the Arctic, the death and horror brought to one of the world's last wildernesses. Are we seriously contemplating taking that risk with the Antarctic? Can nowhere be left as nature intended, its beauty and way of life allowed to remain undesecrated by man?
>
> The thin end of the wedge has already been inserted – with pollutants in the sea and rubbish from human visitors littering the pristine snow. For once let us draw back before it is too late.
>
> **VIRGINIA MCKENNA**
> Actress

The Antarctic treaty was signed in 1959 and ratified in 1961 by 12 countries. Its object was to diffuse growing and potentially explosive territorial claims, some of which overlap. The continent is currently administered under the 1959 Antarctic Treaty. There are now 25 full members, known as 'Consultative Parties'. Seven of these, including the UK, claim segments of Antarctica as sovereign territory. As well as 'freezing' all territorial claims to keep the peace, the Treaty forbids military activity, bans nuclear explosions and radioactive waste disposal, and mandates international co-operation and freedom of scientific inquiry.

The Minerals Treaty is a proposed international agreement which would establish rules for the Antarctic Treaty nations to explore and develop oil and mineral resources likely to be present in Antarctica. The ratification of such a treaty is seen

> Antarctica should remain a place for peaceful scientific activity and co-operation between all nations.
>
> **ANDREA BOARDMAN**
> Radio Personality

by conservationists as the first step in allowing mining and drilling to proceed.

Environmental organisations believe that instead of an increase in exploitation, there should be an *Environment Protection Treaty* for Antarctica which would effectively create an *International World Wilderness Park* allowing only scientific research and limited tourism. Already, France, Australia, Italy and Belgium have backed this idea, but many of the other nations, including the UK, are still in favour of allowing mineral development.

It isn't a case any more of the threat to Antarctica being a 'worthwhile cause' for a small group of activities. It is now cause for great concern to all of us, the whole global community. We must not let the powers that be choose to plunder the resources of Antarctica to the detriment of the animals and their habitat. When man makes mistakes, they are mainly irreversible. We cannot afford to make any more.

I feel strongly that we must all protect this world from governments who for their own ends are prepared to ransack *our* world of beauty and ultimately its longevity.

CLAIRE HACKETT
Actress

The Antarctic Minerals Treaty will not come into operation unless it is ratified by at least 16 countries. including the USA, USSR and all seven claimant countries (Argentina, Australia, Chile, France, New Zealand, Norway and the UK). Australia and France's opposition, therefore, mean that it is effectively vetoed. It should be replaced by an *Environment Protection Treaty*. Other countries should be persuaded to support the idea of protection and conservation – particularly the UK, whose lead many countries are likely to follow.

HANDS
OFF
ANTARCTICA

PETER WILKINSON

I like to think of Antarctica when I'm under pressure. It's bleak, it's wild and it's rugged. Such strong visualisation of this wilderness place has a calming influence on my mind. I'd like to think of Antarctica not so much as being conquered by man, but being understood, appreciated and conserved by man.

PETER HAIGH
TV and Radio Broadcaster

Discarded oil drums on the shorelines

If we can't protect the integrity of an unspoiled continent, what hope have we of clearing up the rest of the world? Environmental consultant Pete Wilkinson *has been to the Antarctic with* Greenpeace, *and puts an in-depth case for protection.*

The Southern Ocean is a dangerous and awesome place. It sweeps around the globe, uninterrupted by land masses, with swells as much as half a mile apart. Sixty knot winds can whip seas into a fury and plunge ships into 40 foot troughs. Plying such waters in a steel-hulled vessel, festooned with antennae and powered by huge diesel motors is an experience indeed; but for those who pioneered the Southern Ocean in wooden sailing vessels, the voyages must have been terrifying.

Cook was beaten back in 1768 by pack ice as he sought 'Terra Australis'. Only in 1840 did Sir James Clark Ross finally crunch his way through the outer pack ice fringing the clear summer waters of the sea which now bears his name, to sail to Ross Island. His route south was eventually blocked by a wall of ice averaging 100 feet in height and stretching nearly 400 miles across, which he called the Great Ice Barrier. He had reached 78 degrees south, a mere 720 miles from the pole.

Seventy years later Scott and Amundsen both crossed this barrier and reached the pole. At that time only a fraction of the Antarctic coast was charted, but the dreadful fate of Scott's expedition thrust the southernmost continent violently into modern consciousness.

The age of discovery gave way to science. Permanent bases were established in Antarctica. Aircraft, in no more than eight hours flew to a land which for long had been a myth. Nations laid their claims, and a resource-hungry world eyed Antarctica's potential mineral wealth.

After the Southern Ocean, the Ross Sea can seem a haven of calm. It is flanked to the west by Victorialand, topped with the largely unclimbed peaks of the Trans-Antarctic Mountains. Coulman Island, Franklin Island and Beaufort Islands rise sharply from the sea, marking the passage south. Even in late December, floes of sea ice still jam the passage to McMurdo Sound and Cape Evans on Ross Island. In 1986, the Southern Quest, a ship following Scott's Scott expedition vessel, was trapped between two huge floes of ice and sunk within a matter of minutes.

Icebergs of great proportions ply the Ross Sea with impunity. 'B9' is a recently separated chunk of the Ross Ice Shelf measuring 90 by 22kms. It contains the indentation known as the Bay of Whales, from where Amundsen made his bid for the pole. Measuring up to 900 feet deep, B9 scours the sea bed and regularly goes aground. The largest iceberg on record was the size of Belgium. The Ross Sea is clearly not a place to trifle with.

The fast ice on McMurdo Sound is as far as a ship can travel. Steaming down the channel cut by US coastguard ice-breakers, you arrive at McMurdo, the base run by the Americans. Here, beneath the ice, lie thousands of pipes, obsolete machinery and beer cans. Winterquarters Bay is biologically poisoned by the chemical without which humanity seems unable to live. This mini-city, which supports 800 people in the summer and a wintering team of 200, is an American scientific base.

McMurdo is the largest of the Antarctic bases. Fifty more dot the continent, while a large geodesic dome marks the US South Polar Base. Perhaps the most spectacular base is that of the Soviets at Leningradskaya, perched on top of the 1000 feet high Mt. Lenin. Below the mountain lie what one would think were hundreds of basking seals. On closer inspection, they reveal themselves to be discarded oil drums, casually tossed over the precipice. Over the years thousands more must have drifted away with the sea ice.

The Chinese use a melt-lake as a rubbish tip. The French base was carefully sited next to an environmentally important archipelago. Now they are blasting the very penguins they came to study from their nesting sites to make way for an airstrip. The Argentinians have a bank and a small hotel, encourage families to live in the Antarctic and even claim the first ever 'Antarctican' who was born at their peninsula base in 1978.

Argentina, Chile and the UK have overlapping claims in the peninsula, and the Falklands war had as much to do with access to the Antarctic as it did with upholding the rights of the British community on that far-flung rock.

The greatest threat to Antarctica is mining. Quite apart from the damage an oil spill would create, the influx of people during the summer months, the need for shore-based facilities and the importance of equipment would all destabilise the continent's vulnerable ecological web. The US National Science Foundation, which operates McMurdo, opposes private expeditions, since they pose an unwelcome burden on their rescue facilities. Yet faced with the invasion of hundreds of oil-industry people who are unused to Antarctic conditions, the NSF is silent.

Last year the supply vessel, *Bahia Paraiso*, spilled 100,000 gallons of light fuel oil near the US Palmer station, wiping out years of scientific work designed to study ozone depletion. Many scientists recognise that industrialisation would spell the end of other scientific projects which rely on near-pristine conditions, but only a few have spoken out against the threat of mining in the Antarctic.

If mining is the threat of the future, the activities of the past have already harmed the continent's marine species. Seals, whales and penguins were mercilessly persecuted in the 18th and 19th centuries. On Macquarie Island, the pots in which penguins were boiled down still exist, as do the buildings and rotting ships of the whaling industry on South Georgia. In recent years, Antarctic wildlife has been afforded protection, yet despite the International Whaling Commission ban, the last of the great whales are still hunted by Japan.

To witness the death of a whale is a harrowing experience. The stillness and tranquillity of the Antarctic is shattered by the explosive charge which sends the harpoon at 60 mph into the yielding flesh of the whale. On entry, a further explosive charge in the head of the harpoon forces four barbs out into the flesh. The whale sounds, pulling the wire hawser taut. Winches

It is not true that every Japanese supports research whaling, as the whaling industry and the Japanese government are trying to convince people overseas.

DR ROGER PAYNE
Senior Scientist, Worldwide Fund for Nature, and Director, Long Term Research Institute

on the whaler turn, reeling in the stricken beast. The animal quivers and thrashes in its death-throes as it is hauled up against the ship. Two electrodes are lowered from the high bow and the whale succumbs at last. It is transferred to the low-slung side of the ship and hawsers fasten the creature by the tail. A nearby factory vessel drags the animal up its slipway, whereupon its mouth falls open, spilling water and blood. On board, the corpse is set about by 20 workers with curved flensing knives and within minutes it is being processed, frozen and boxed.

> Four species of whales are practically extinct through whaling, and several species of fin fish are commercially extinct through over-fishing. What shall we exterminate next?
>
> **CLAIRE RAYNER**
> TV Personality

Whales are still slaughtered for 'scientific' reasons

Fin whale.
The fin whale feeds on krill
and small crustacea

Right whale.
The right whale (southern)
leaps out of the water
performing an impressive
courtship display

Southern bottlenose whale.
The southern bottlenose
whale has a beak-like jaw.
It feeds mainly on squid

Blue whale.
The blue whale is the largest
creature that the world has seen. It
feeds on krill in Antarctic waters
but unfortunately is on the
endangered species list. Because of
its size, it was the most profitable
for whaling fleets.

Minke whale.
The minke whale is the
smallest baleen whale,
feeding on krill.
It is being slaughtered
despite a moratorium on
whaling

*Humpback whale.
The humpback whale is so
called because it arches its
back before diving*

*Sei whale.
The sei whale stays in deep
waters, feeding on fast-
swimming prey such as
Antarctic herring*

*Orca whale.
The orca whale is the
largest of all
carnivores and feeds
on seals and penguins*

*Sperm whale.
The sperm whale is the largest of
the toothed whales with a large
head, a third of its body size*

The Southern Ocean is possibly the most abundant in marine species – many of which are unknown to man. Is it right that we should allow these teeming waters to be overfished and polluted?

ANNEKA RICE
TV Personality

Japan claims that minke whales are numerous in Antarctic waters, yet it was unable last year to meet its self-imposed quota of 330. Compared to reports by the early Antarctic voyagers of veritable carpets of whales from horizon to horizon, the modern traveller sees them relatively infrequently and only in small pods.

Krill are small, shrimp-like creatures which exist in huge swarms in Antarctic waters. One swarm was estimated to contain over 2 million tonnes and covered an area of 400 sq kms. They are the staple diet of the baleen whales, which take mouthfuls of sea water and use their baleen plates as filters. Krill are the corner-stone of the Antarctic marine food-chain.

In the event of an oil spill, krill would be seriously at risk, but they face a more immediate threat in the shape of fishing. Current catch levels are modest; however, once processing technologies have been developed sufficiently, there are plans to increase the catch of krill, perhaps by as much as 6000 per cent. The admirable Convention on the Conservation of Antarctic Marine Living Resources requires a 'total impact' assessment to be made when setting catch limits, but in practice the Convention is crippled by the lack of base-line data. The impact of an increased catch of krill could only be guessed at, for despite the existence of the Convention, fishing in Antarctic waters is effectively unregulated. Several species of fish are known to be at ten per cent of their estimated 1969 levels, while the Antarctic cod is commercially extinct.

One of the scientific bases in Antarctica

It was Theodore Roosevelt who, at the beginning of this century, said 'Nine-tenths of wisdom is being wise in time'. For Antarctica and its wildlife this could not be more true. When the Antarctic Treaty is reviewed, the future of this continent may be decided in a few moments. The mineral resources, if they are exploited, will last for little longer than that. For the minke whales – still hunted mercilessly – time is running out. Scientists are caught in a race against time to provide answers to the questions posed by global warming and the potentially disastrous consequences of pollution.

The time has come for a change in attitude, for nations to direct their attention to conservation, not to commercial interests. And for individuals to support environmental protection. Next time you look into a mirror and are reminded of the passage of time, remember Antarctica. It needs, for all of us, to be preserved for all time.

CHRISSIE PAINELL
Health and Beauty Editor, Cosmopolitan

Antarctica is a place of great beauty, a place which invigorates the soul and which at the same time carries out a critical role in regulating weather and affecting the natural features of the southern hemisphere. The choice facing us as an international community is whether to protect or destroy it. There are no half-measures. Protection means declaring the continent a World Park where all activity is monitored, where tourism is controlled, where krill and fish are afforded total protection for at least ten years, where whales and other marine mammals can find absolute sanctuary, where the siting and operation of bases is closely regulated, and where mining is quite simply forbidden.

Returning from the Antarctic is as powerful an experience as going there. You can smell land from a hundred miles away. The first sight of greenery after the long weeks of greys, whites, blacks and purples is exhilarating and Scott's words – 'God, this is an awful place' – take a new meaning. But for all the normality of civilisation, Antarctica, once seen and experienced, has a magnetic quality about it.

Of all the politicians, diplomats and oil-company representatives who sit around behind closed doors pontificating on the fate of this continent, how many, one wonders, have ever been there?

5

WILDLIFE

ROBERT HUGHES

Will man learn anything? The innocent ocean and wildlife slowly die in his shadow and he lets it happen.

GLENDA JACKSON
Actress

The point where the warmer waters from the Indian, Pacific and Atlantic Oceans meet the cold Antarctic waters is known as the Antarctic Convergence. Here conditions are ideal for the development of phytoplankton.

Phytoplankton is the first link in the simple foodchain which supports the abundance of marine life in the Southern Ocean. The microscopic floating plants use the Antarctic summer sunlight to provide food for the zooplankton, of which krill is the staple variety.

The Antarctic krill is a shrimp-like crustacean, and forms an important food source for many of the Antarctic species

Krill can be found in swarms south of the Antarctic Convergence, forming the basic food for all higher forms of life, including squid, fish, seals, penguins and whales. Commercial exploitation of krill has been taking place unhindered since the 1960s. Despite scientific research, too little is known about the krill's life cycle to afford much knowledge about the effects of this exploitation on the marine ecosystem. Its high protein content and resource potential have made this shrimp-like crustacean an important human and animal food source for countries like Japan, the Soviet Union, Bulgaria, East Germany and Poland.

The high density of the swarms make high catch rates relatively easy, and this has lead to over-fishing. With the decline in the whale populations due to exploitation, the apparent krill surplus has lead to a keenness to increase krill fishing quotas. If fishing continues at present levels, the recovery of the whale populations could be made even more difficult. The entire food chain is being threatened by a continual extraction of its most basic and important element.

Around 100 species of fish have been identified in Antarctic waters but again, little is known of life cycle and growth rates. The fish have adapted to polar temperatures and have a special 'anti-freeze' component in their body fluids. Several species have been commercially fished in the past, including Antarctic cod and herring, but numbers have declined to a point where these species are now commercially extinct. The level of fin fish stock generally is uncertain, and more research is needed to evaluate current numbers. Squid also, have not escaped the commercial nets, and countries like Spain are interested in the significant catches available in Antarctic waters. Again, little is known of current stock and more research is required before over-exploitation occurs.

Possibly the worst case of exploitation and near extinction through man's presence in Antarctica has been the effects of the whaling industry. In its heyday, over 30,000 blue whales were being slaughtered per season. Huge whaling ships, like small villages, slaughtered the whales in thousands, sending explosive charges and harpoons into the mammals, then hauling them on board, to be cut up and processed in boxes as whale meat, to feed Japan and the Soviet Union. All attempts to 'regulate' the whaling catches were ignored, despite the knowledge that the whales were being driven to extinction. In the mid-seventies, despite growing world pressure to stop, Japan and the Soviet Union were the only nations operating in Antarctic waters, still taking 30,000 whales per season.

Until the moratorium on commercial whaling came into force in 1986, Japan was still slaughtering up to 3,000 whales a season. Even now, the moratorium is in force, and Japan is continuing to whale, ostensibly for scientific purposes. Seventy pounds sterling per lb is the value of whale meat in Tokyo department stores, and whaling is still continuing. A huge Japanese factory ship is currently hunting out the few remaining whales in Antarctic waters – turning its attentions to the smaller species because the larger ones are already dead, and insisting that commercial quotas should be resumed.

Protect Antarctica from the proposed Minerals Treaty and let there be an International World Wilderness Park instead, which can protect whales, fish and other wildlife. We need to control and evaluate the impact of all human activities, including waste disposal.

Ban all whaling and fin fishing and stop the Japanese exploiting a loop-hole by being allowed to whale for scientific purposes. Gourmet restaurants don't employ scientists!

TOYAH WILCOX
Singer/Actress

Whale population studies are difficult to conduct because of the large areas involved and the lack of detailed knowledge about migratory patterns. A report released by the Scientific Committee of the International Whaling Commission at last year's annual conference confirmed the worst possible predictions of whale populations. The blue whale, possibly the nearest to extinction, was once believed to number 250,000. Now as few as 500 survive. So few in fact, that it is not likely that the species will survive. This, the largest mammal the world has ever known, may very well die out forever. Fin whale populations have also plummeted from approximately 500,000 to 2,000. The population of 1,250,000 sperm whales has dropped to approximately 4,000.

Unreliable methods of counting whale populations are used by whaling nations in an attempt to prove that their continued whaling actions are justified.

The advancements man has made in the twentieth century have been extraordinary. Developments in communication, travel, science and medicine have been sometimes miraculous and yet, *never* has the world been at greater risk. Man is the world's greatest enemy; this century has witnessed the advancement of man to the extent of his being capable of destroying the world. There is now war, famine, natural disasters, pollution on a scale never witnessed before. In fact 'the end is nigh' is no longer just a quaint Biblical saying. Man is a greedy, aggressive, insecure species – always wanting more, believing satisfaction is close by.

Man is also capable of love and compassion. I pray that he may become more vulnerable and develop the courage to display more love, care and compassion. The destruction of Antarctica, if man causes it to occur, will be the beginning of the end of the world. Exaggeration? Don't try it just to prove me wrong!

DAVID SUCHET
Actor

This year, (1990), the International Whaling Commission meets in the Netherlands to discuss the current ban on commercial whaling and existing Minke whale population figures. There will be great pressure from Japan, Norway and Iceland to resume whaling. You can make your views known by writing to the relevant embassies.

Since the 1960s, when seal hunting ended, the seal populations have been steadily increasing. The numbers of ross, leopard, elephant, southern fur, weddell and crabeater seals now represent two-thirds of the world's entire population of seals.

Anyone wishing to write with comments about current whaling and fishing practices in Antarctica is urged to do so. The addresses are:

The Ambassador Embasssy of Japan 101–104 Piccadilly London W1V 9FN	The Ambassador Embassy of Japan 112 Empire Circuit Yarralumba A.C.T. Australia 2600	The Ambassador Embassy of Japan P.O. Box 6340 Wellington New Zealand

The Ambassador
Embassy of the
  U.S.S.R.
18 Kensington
  Palace Gardens
London
W8
	The Ambassador
	Embassy of the
	  U.S.S.R.
	78 Canberra Avenue
	Griffith
	A.C.T.
	Australia 2603
		The Ambassador
		Embassy of the
		  U.S.S.R.
		57 Messines Road
		Karon
		Wellington
		New Zealand

The Ambassador
Royal Norwegian
  Embassy
25 Belgrave Square
London
SW1X 8QD
	The Ambassador
	Royal Norwegian
	  Embassy
	17 Hunter Street
	Yarralumba
	A.C.T.
	Australia 2600
		Honorary Consul
		  General
		Norwegian
		  Consulate
		P.O. Box 1990
		Wellington
		New Zealand

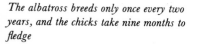

The albatross breeds only once every two years, and the chicks take nine months to fledge

Crabeater seals feed predominantly on krill, eating up to 63 million tonnes a year, but the other seal species eat fish and squid. Leopard seals also eat penguins and other birds. Seals are well insulated against freezing air and water temperatures. A warm and dense coat of fur as well as a layer of blubber beneath the skin ensure that the animal is well protected.

Birds comprise a significant part of the Antarctic ecosystem, particularly in summer. Although there are only 40 species, they number approximately 180 million in all. They are mainly confined to the coastal regions, pack ice and sub-Antarctic islands.

The brown skua with its chick. These are notorious predators, raiding penguin colonies for eggs and young birds

Penguins and seals live in colonies on the narrow, ice-free strip of coastal land. The populations are abundant, supported by the rich waters of the Southern Ocean. There are seven species of penguin in the Antarctic. Adelié is the most abundant, gentoo probably the fastest swimmer of all birds, macaroni found only on the outer and inner Antarctic islands, chinstrap – smallest of the 'brush-tailed' species, rockhopper (an agressive creature), king and emperor, the latter the largest species, four feet in height. However, on the narrow strip of ice-free coastal land, the colonies have to compete with research stations, airstrips and ship docking areas.

I suppose like most people, I know very little about the South Pole or the North Pole. Previously I thought of the Antarctic as being a great barren waste of snow and ice. This year I have had my eyes opened, particularly by my manager, Neville Shulman. He journeyed to the North Pole in 1989 to witness the creation of ice sculptures by a British sculptor who himself had travelled to the Arctic to spend a month with the Inuits. He made me realise how beautiful and unique the ends of the world are and why it is essential that we do everything in our power to protect them. I have always been a strong supporter of the campaigns to save the seal and whale populations and of course I am appalled to learn that in the Antarctic the penguin, the most comic and gentle of creatures, is also under threat. All areas of natural beauty must be protected. Solitude has its own special draw and now I have started to understand why men and women are prepared to walk for weeks and months across frozen white terrain in order to feel themselves part of these magical, mysterious environments.

TWIGGY LAWSON
Actress

These mammals are easily disturbed, as one would imagine, by bulldozers and helicopters. The activities of man on these colonial grounds are nothing short of outrageous. So appalling was the environmental damage of the French airstrip construction that a similar project currently being undertaken by the British has involved a conservationist being flown in to act as a 'watch dog', with freedom to report on all building activities.

The concentration of PCBs is so high in Winterquarters Bay that the safest solution would be to cement it. So much for nature conservation!

PAULA YATES
TV Personality

The effects of man's pollution in Antarctica provides an added hazard for all wildlife, both on land and in th sea. Huge open pits of rubbish and dumps of mechanical refuse are scattered over the land. Much of the disused machinery is moved onto melting ice floes, to disappear conveniently out of sight and mind.

A chinstrap penguin with the distinctive black 'strap' around its chin, protecting the young bird

PCBs (polychlorinated biphenyls) have been introduced through the use of machine oils and equipment, and when the machines are discarded, the PCBs go with them – into a lake, or into the sea. PCBs are man-made pollutants which are not easily disposed of, but which can poison wildlife when introduced into the food chain. The level of PCBs and heavy metals such as mercury and cadmium are so high in Winterquarters Bay, an area adjacent to the USA McMurdo base station, that conservationists have suggested the safest method of disposal would be to cement over the area.

For a continent which is looked upon by most people as a wilderness of ice and wildlife, Antarctica is already suffering from the increasing encroachment of man. This must be regulated in order to stop further pollution.

6

THREATS TO
ANTARCTICA
A Silver Lining In
The Oil Slicks?

CASSANDRA PHILLIPS

Three shipwrecks in recent months, two off Antarctica and one off Alaska, have given the world a dramatic foretaste of what could happen if the Antarctic were to be opened up to mining and oil exploitation as Alaska has been.

The question of whether Antarctica – so far the only part of the world free from industrial activity – should be exploited by the oil companies and other miners, is a matter of conflict at the moment. The member states of the Antarctic Treaty are deciding whether to ratify the recently negotiated Convention on the Regulation of Antarctic Mineral Resource Activities (CRAMRA). The Convention does contain fairly strong environmental safeguards, but if it is ratified it would have the effect of making mining and oil development legally practicable in the Antarctic for the first time.

It would be only a matter of time, however fantastic the resources discovered in Antarctica, before they too expired and further, irretrievable damage was done to our planet. Now is the moment, then, to decide to leave our last chance, our one virgin spot of earth, alone. Whilst, therefore, giving a glimmer of hope to the earth, we should surge forth and find other ways to survive. It's simple, really; either we start afresh now, or we start afresh later, when we've used up all our wishes.

CAROL ROYLE
Actress

Overhanging ice and icicles on the shore at Cape Adare, constantly changing shapes fashioned by the elements

Meanwhile, the warning of environmental organisations, to the effect that the risks of allowing mineral development in the vulnerable Antarctic environment are too great, have proved fully justified. First, on 28 January 1989, the ship *Bahia Paraiso* ran aground on well-charted rocks off the Antarctic Peninsula. The *Bahia Paraiso* was an Argentinian ship carrying supplies and tourists to Argentinian bases. The 315 passengers and crew were all rescued, but four days later the ship sank, and much of its 250,000 gallons of diesel fuel, plus 150 barrels of oil destined for Antarctic scientific bases, spilled into the sea. The accident happened only two kilometres from the US Palmer Research Station and a protected area especially rich in penguins, seals and other wildlife, where biological research had been in progress for twenty years. Although the ship was wrecked at the height of the Antarctic summer and in the climatically least extreme part of Antarctica, it nevertheless took a further six days before a ship carrying US oil-spill equipment arrived to start the very expensive clean-up operation.

Antarctica remains a shining image of natural purity, but man's unnatural greed for oil and minerals could shatter it in decades. If we can't say no here, what's safe?

SUSANNAH YORK
Actress

A chinstrap penguin with its young. The young birds leave the colony within nine weeks

Then, as penguins, skuas, krill and other wildlife began to die from oil contamination, the brief Antarctic summer drew to a close, and attempts to salvage the *Bahia Paraiso* had to be postponed for a further seven to eight months, leaving the risk of even more pollution from the oil remaining in the ship's tanks. Although some of the diesel oil will have evaporated, what remains is especially poisonous to marine life. Moreover, all oil spills are more harmful in cold seas, because microbes take longer to degrade oil at low temperatures and globules of oil trapped in the ice take many years to disperse. The tragic effects of the *Bahia Paraiso* wreck could well be evident 100 years from now.

The second, less widely reported shipwreck was of a small Peruvian ship, the *Humboldt*, which ran aground and began leaking oil on 26 February off King George's Island, near the northernmost part of the Antarctic Peninsula. Reports indicated that the ship was most unsuited to withstand Antarctica's icy seas and should never have been sent there.

These accidents took place in Antarctica, serving as examples of the likely consequences of human activity, even when this is apparently as environmentally benign as scientific research and small-scale tourism. As if these examples were not enough, on 24 March 1989, a further lesson followed in the inevitable consequence of large-scale oil extraction in extreme environments. The fully laden supertanker *Exxon Valdez* ran into a submerged reef in Prince William Sound, Alaska, and eight of the ship's oil tanks were punctured. The ship was only two years old, the weather was calm, the route well-charted and the captain was experienced. (Apparently, however, he was intoxicated.)

Paradise Bay on the Antarctic Peninsula

Antarctica – the mention of that great white silence is like recalling a perfect symphony. It's like an environmental miser's bank; it's nice to know it's there: a giant white wilderness that so far has avoided the ravages of *homo sapiens*. Down the centuries it has stayed virgin, giving sustenance to those wild creatures that do not desecrate its flawless beauty. And it has something that Western civilisation has lost – *Silence*. The scales of nature are balanced to perfection. Alas! as I write, idiots, scientists, industrialists, and politicians are planning to exploit this pristine paradise: they know that an increasingly *over-populated* planet is ready to purchase the products: oil, minerals, fish, in fact anything and everything the continent contains. The robbery will turn Antarctica into the appalling neurotic, crowded, cramped, polluted rubbish tip that is called western civilisation.

SPIKE MILLIGAN
Comedian, Author

What followed has been well publicised because the journalists, if not the officials capable of taking emergency action, were able to reach the scene without delay. During the following weeks, 11 million gallons of oil leaked from the *Exxon Valdez* and spread over thousands of square kilometres of previously unpolluted beaches, shoreline and islands. Descriptions of oil-krilled fish, sea-otters, sea-birds, seals, even bald eagles, Sitka deer and bears trying to feed on the filthy beaches, were soon reported around the world. They were followed by descriptions of chaos in the clean-up operations, labelled an 'organisational disaster', with authority divided between state, federal and Exxon corporation officials. The US$100 million a year commercial fishery was shut down and tourists replaced by clean-up volunteers. The spill exemplified the inability of oil companies to respond promptly and efficiently to large oil spills in remote areas.

Antarctica is lonely, beautiful and unique. As one of the last truly unspoilt natural environments in the world, its preservation and protection is absolutely vital and we must all work to secure that.

MATTHEW TAYLOR MP
(Truro)

Cape Crozier, Ross Island, Southern Antarctica

I have never been to the Antarctic continent, and I doubt that I ever will. As a traveller I've been lucky enough to push by foot, horse, bicycle or ski into some of the more remote corners of the world. By Antarctic standards, these journeys have been inhospitable climates and populated parts. My wide-eyed and fancy-free wanderings through the Hindu Kush, Tibetan Plateau, Andes, Africa, Gobi Desert and Lapland have always been made in the knowledge that there was one place in the world which would always be out of bounds; which was *so* remote and *so* purely inhospitable for man that it would remain inaccessible to anything but the imagination. Life on earth will become very much duller and more dangerous once we have proved that we have the capability to defile even the White Continent.

NICK CRANE
Explorer

Warnings of the environmental risks of oil exploitation in Alaska had been given for years, yet disaster still struck for entirely human reasons. The tanker captain was drunk (and an inexperienced crewman was in charge of the vessel), Exxon responded to the spill far too slowly, and the technology available for cleaning-up was inadequate. Prince William Sound is remote, environmentally unspoilt and ecologically fragile compared with many other oil tanker routes at lower latitudes, but compared with the Antarctic it is easily accessible and has a benign climate. The sea does not even freeze over in winter, let alone all year round.

Crabeater seals, one of the world's most abundant large mammals, on an iceflow

If oil exploitation is ever permitted in Antarctica, sooner or later the *Bahia Paraiso* and *Exxon Valdez* disasters will be repeated there and the consequences will be even more tragic. The phrase that conservationists least enjoy saying is 'We told you so'. The hope is that some good will result from the shipwrecks if the lessons are taken to heart and oil and mineral development are banned in the Antarctic.

Cassandra Phillips is the chairperson of the UK Wildlife Link Antarctic Group.

Antarctica is separated from the rest of the world by an unfriendly barrier of ice. The surrounding Southern Ocean is stormy and tempestuous, warning off unwelcome travellers. Although home to millions of birds and mammals, this is no place for man. Nature will send its ice floe warriors to protect it against oil prospectors. The seas will flow black with the spills of its spoils.

CARON KEATING
TV Personality

7

NO
MINING
IN
ANTARCTICA

SIR PETER SCOTT,
CH, CBE, DSC, FRS

The following article by Sir Peter Scott was published in *The Breconshire Naturalist*, in Autumn 1989.

One of the issues with which I am most concerned at the moment is the future of Antarctica. Because of my father's expeditions and his death there in 1911 when I was two years old, it has always been a very special part of the world for me. I have had the great good fortune to have been there five times, and even without my family connections I would have been fascinated by it as a naturalist and as a conservationist.

In almost every way Antarctica is extraordinarily beautiful and awe-inspiring. Everyone knows it is the coldest part of the earth, but it is also the windiest and the driest part, even though much of it is covered by ice over a mile thick. Apart from mosses and lichens, only two species of flowering plant live there, but the surrounding seas are amongst the most fertile and biologically productive in the world. The Southern Ocean supports an almost unbelievable abundance of birds and seals, as well as

The sperm whale is the largest of the toothed whales – the male can grow up to 18m (60ft) and weigh up to 70 tonnes

whales, fish and squid, all directly or indirectly dependent on krill, the shrimplike, 7cm-long crustacean *Euphausia superba*. Antarctic krill form dense swarms during the summer, sometimes several miles across. At night the swarms light up, and become a mass of living blue-green fire.

Politically, too, Antarctica is unique. It is administered by the Antarctic Treaty, signed in 1959 by 12 countries including the UK, and now joined by 10 more full 'Consultative Parties'. Partly because of the contentious sovereignty issues, the Antarctic Treaty did not say anything about mineral exploitation. The Treaty Parties agreed that this question would have to be settled in a separate Convention, and meanwhile there should be a moratorium on any prospecting and mining.

In June 1988 diplomats from all the Treaty Parties agreed the text of an Antarctic Minerals Convention, after tough negotiations spread over six years. The Convention will come into force only if it is ratified by at least 16 countries, including USSR and USA and all seven countries that claim slices of Antarctica (Argentina, Australia, Chile, France, New Zealand, Norway and the UK). Although the Convention contains very strict environmental controls, I believe that the risks are much too great ever to justify any mineral activities in the Antarctic. There can be no doubt that the fragile terrestrial and marine eco-systems would be degraded for a very long time (centuries, rather than decades) by mining, oil and gas exploitation, and all the associated infrastructure that would accompany these activities. The wilderness value of the Antarctic would be lost forever, and for a strictly finite, short-term gain. In the case of oil, the 'gain' would not only be finite, but would actually be harmful to the world environment. Assuming the oil was used as a fuel, it would only add to the global warming resulting from the build-up of CO_2 and other greenhouse gases.

At the end of January 1989, an Argentinian ship carrying supplies and tourists to Antarctic bases was wrecked off the Antarctic Peninsula, and much of its 250,000 gallons of diesel fuel spilled into the sea just next to an area especially rich in penguins, seals and other wildlife. Then, on 23 March the *Exxon Valdez* ran aground off the Alaskan coast, and over the next few weeks 11 million gallons of oil leaked out and spread over thousands of square miles of

Mining activities on shore would have to compete for space with wildlife. The narrow strip of coastal land is where many birds, seals and penguins live and breed. These areas, abundant with marine life, would be disturbed by oil tankers and support ships.

ANTHEA TURNER
TV and Radio Personality

Rather than looking to Antarctica to supply us with today's commodities, we should invest in this one remaining natural asset in order to find ways to protect our own future.

SARAH LAWSON
Actress

previously pristine Arctic shoreline and islands. These two events had a great influence on the countries in the process of deciding whether to ratify the Antarctic Minerals Convention, as they proved that all the controls in the world could not prevent accidents and could not clear up oil spilt in such harsh conditions.

The first country to react was Australia, which announced that it would not sign the Minerals Convention, and instead would try to negotiate a comprehensive environmental protection convention for Antarctica. It has since been joined by both France and Belgium in calling for the Antarctic to be made an International Wilderness Reserve. These are very exciting developments. Sadly, in my view, the UK government still supports the Minerals Convention and would like to keep open the option of mining in the last great wilderness on earth. I am convinced that, instead, we must work for agreement that no mining or oil drilling will ever be allowed there and the whole continent should be declared a wilderness reserve. It would still be used as an international scientific laboratory, would be kept free of all military weapons and nuclear activities, the birds and mammals would be protected and tourism would be carefully controlled.

The tide of public opinion in the world is flowing so strongly now in favour of preserving rather than polluting our planet, that I believe it will be possible to negotiate such an agreement.

Slimbridge, July 1989.

I have been lucky enough to visit Antarctica four times – each time as a controlled tourist with Lindblad Travel. People ask why I should want to go to such a cold and unfriendly place. The answer is simple: it is incredibly beautiful. It is a very elemental place – white-outs, severe gales with high seas, brilliant sunshine and unpredictable weather. That is all part of the wilderness atmosphere. There are very few areas near the shoreline where boats may land. These areas, which are rocky beaches during the southern summer, are the breeding grounds of the proper inhabitants of this icy continent – the penguins. Antarctica is truly the last great wilderness on this planet. It should remain so. It was the greatest wish of my husband, the late Sir Peter Scott, that it should be made a World Park.

LADY PHILIPPA SCOTT

Adelié penguins are the most abundant and widely distributed of all penguin species

One by one, we are destroying the world's life support systems. Half the tropical forests are already gone and scientists at the Smithsonian Institute in Washington now fear that the vast Amazonian rainforest will be destroyed or irreparably damaged within ten years. Meanwhile, depleted ozone levels in the atmosphere above Antarctica have begun to expose marine life to intensified levels of ultraviolet radiation and could bring about the collapse of the entire marine food chain. We are truly on the edge of a global catastrophe and we must change – or perish.

BRYN JONES
Chairman, Landbank Trust

Sir Peter Scott, who has been referred to as the patron saint of conservation, died in August 1989 just two weeks before his eightieth birthday. It was his wish that after his death an appeal – the Peter Scott Memorial Appeal – should be launched to ensure that the work he began to save endangered species and their habitats could continue. He wanted the money raised by that appeal to be divided equally between the two organisations he founded, and which he helped to make into conservation groups of world stature: the Wildfowl and Wetlands Trust and The Worldwide Fund for Nature.

The Peter Scott Memorial Appeal for Conservation is one of

It is a very sad fact that human beings seem determined to destroy both themselves and the planet in which they live. This can never be changed until concern replaces greed. Let's start by involving school children and hope that they at least will want to survive.

JEAN BOHT
Actress

the beneficiaries of the sale of this book. The money which goes to the Memorial Appeal will be spent on conservation projects which Sir Peter Scott himself considered particularly important, such as protecting the threatened places where endangered birds and other animals live, and educating the next generation about the need to ensure that our planet's living natural resources are not destroyed.

White Land, White Solace
People imagine that actors are a gregarious lot by nature, but all actors I know are lonely at heart and the mask of bonhomie they wear in public is no different from the masks and make-up they wear at work, and for all of them there is a solitary landscape in their minds to which they retreat to find their heartsease.

When I was a little boy I heard Vaughan William's 7th Symphony: his 'Sinfonia Antarctica'. The austerity of the music captivated me at once, summoning up so perfectly the peerless majesty of the white, empty landscape and its extraordinary severity and loveliness. I think of Antarctica often; I dream of Antarctica. The idea that its beauty should be violated by man, for whatever daft purpose, is intolerable. It is our last true unexploited wilderness. For all our sakes it *must* be protected and preserved.

KEITH BAXTER
Actor

Sperm whales

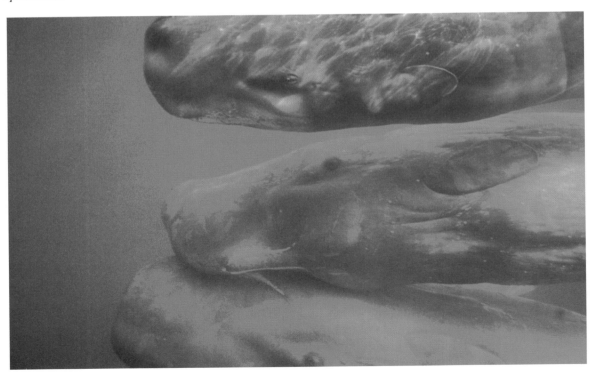

The other beneficiaries from the sale of the book are:

THE WHALE AND DOLPHIN CONSERVATION SOCIETY was set up in 1987 to raise funds for and promote awareness of threatened cetaceans, (whales, dolphins and porpoises). Money raised pays for reports and bulletins, plus scientific assignments to protect endangered species.

WILDLIFE LINK is the UK-based liaison body established in 1980 for national and international voluntary organisations concerned with the protection of wildlife. It has 43 members who work in specialist working groups to co-ordinate action on specific issues, eg: The Antarctic Wildlife Group and The Cetacean Group.

THE ANTARCTIC AND SOUTHERN COALITION has bases in Australia, Denmark, New Zealand and USA, and is a campaigning organisation, pushing for permanent protection for Antarctica along the lines of an International World Wilderness Park concept.

THE COUSTEAU SOCIETY headed by Jacques Cousteau and his son Jean-Michel, is campaigning for the protection of Antarctica. A petition was delivered to the French Government supporting the World Wilderness Park principle, and a meeting was held in Washington last September to discuss the same principle.

THE LONG TERM RESEARCH INSTITUTE, run by the eminent scientist Dr Roger Payne, is involved in important studies of whales in the Southern Oceans. Dr Payne was the first person to identify and record songs of the humpback whale and has conducted a study on the southern right whale, which is the second most endangered species in Antarctica.

> If the Antarctic continent were protected we would all know that it is not too late to reverse the trend for world destruction.
>
> **MARK GOODIER**
> TV and Radio Personality

8

ANTARCTICA: THE FUTURE

RICHARD ADAMS

The major concern about the Antarctic is the threat of mineral exploitation by one or more of the foreign powers. The original treaty ratified in 1961 showed a commendable sense of responsibility about he preservation of the environment, but went into no detail about the possible need to control mining and drilling in the future.

Further construction continues, despite opposition

We're astonished that in 1990 the governments of the world still haven't learnt that the major corporations still don't care.

PAUL DANIELS and **DEBBIE MCGEE**
TV Personalities

During the 1970s, when continued acceptance of the treaty was still the subject of international argument, the parties realised that the question of exploitation actually constituted a threat to the treaty system serious enough to break it up altogether. Some maintained that mining would do the environment no harm. Others held that it would, by upsetting ecology and wildlife breeding patterns. The threat of oil-spills, in particular, caused anxiety to environmentalists.

Sovereignty claims in Antarctica are also relevant and these in themselves, it is feared, could form the subject of dispute. Although territorial claims have been shelved for the duration of the treaty, this state of affairs may well not last. Some have put forward the view that mining in Antarctica will be required in order to fulfil world needs as other places run out of resources. The Minerals Convention, it has been argued, could lead to exploration for mining.

Various environmental groups have felt troubled, fearing both ineffective management and interruption to detached scientific observation. The Antarctic, they hold, needs to remain intact so that the effects of world pollution and global warming can be properly watched. The environmental lobby wants a World Wilderness Park – a wildlife sanctuary and scientific preservation area. They are against any notion of mining.

Antarctica contains 90 per cent of the world's ice and most of the planet's fresh water reserves. This frozen watery place holds the key to the levels of pollution in the rest of the world. Knowing that in all its pristine glory, air and water pollution have already reached Antarctica, we should be reversing the pollution process and creating a protection zone around Antarctica.

PHILIP SCHOFIELD
TV and Radio Personality

The ice starts to close in

Some fears have been expressed that global warming will lead to the melting of glaciers and the polar land ice sheets, with a consequent rise in sea levels and the flooding of coastal areas. At present it cannot be said that there is definite evidence of man-made climate change. Over the next 10 or 20 years it may be possible to say that greenhouse gases are causing global warming.

The effect on the Antarctic may be small, since although it is expected that there will be some melting of the Greenland ice, there will be increased snowfall over Antarctica, where temperatures are expected to remain largely below freezing. There have been predictions of the loss of the West Antarctic ice sheet but the ice is anchored solidly offshore by underwater obstructions and its disintegration seems unlikely.

ALAN D SMITH
Private Secretary, Department of the Environment for Northern Ireland

The cliffs of ice tower above the water

Blue ice, I discovered, as opposed to green, is always ice that has broken off a glacier. Water, of course, cannot be compressed, but ice can. Compression causes ice partially to melt and brings about tighter packing of the ice crystals. It is this greater density which causes the ice to refract blue light.

Icebergs are like the stars. They exist remote, in their own places, lifeless, empty, conforming to things like gravity and heat and cold, over time-spans in relation to which a human life is hardly any time at all. They come into existence, change and cease to be, but have no purpose or meaning. However, when you've lived among them for a bit, it's actually human beings who have no meaning. Icebergs are in accord with the universe. We aren't.

RICHARD ADAMS
Author
from 'Voyage through the Antarctic', 1982

In the real world, wild places generally come a distant second to commercial interests and politics, so there is often a feeling of 'inevitability' about the kind of problems facing Antarctica. But there can be no half-measures because the risks of exploitation there are simply too great. We either save Antarctica in its entirety, or we allow the destructive human activities that afflict every other continent in the world to take over. I believe that, apart from the many practical reasons for protecting the region, it has become a choice between material and spiritual values. Our ability to save, or destroy, Antarctica is the ultimate test of our determination to protect the planet.

MARK CARWARDINE
Author

Although there has been much international argument, nothing has yet been decided. All that is preventing mining at present is a voluntary agreement which, it is alleged, has already been breached here and there under the cloak of 'scientific research'. Clearly, a fresh and binding international agreement is needed. Public opinion, following what it understands of reported scientific research, seems to be, for the most part, on the side of environmental preservation. Several matters will need to be resolved during the coming decade:

Can the environmental groups keep up the pressure?

Do we really have to exploit Antarctica to fulfil world needs for mineral resources?

To what extent does naval strategy come into the picture?

How powerful are the industrialists in world politics?

The original agreement of the late 1950s was sensible, based on the concept of flexible international agreement. It will come under test during this decade. The United Nations may well begin to play a leading – possibly a decisive – role.

As nature retreats,
The wilderness fragments
To islands in our hothouse home.

What chance has the virgin
Southern Pole
Unless our soul cries enough –
and we listen?

WILLIAM TRAVERS
Actor

Today, the question of environmental pollution has become far more urgent and publicised than ever it was in the 1950s. It has become the dominant consideration. Until now – apart from the disgraceful business of whaling – the management of the Antarctic has remained a respectable and decent affair. But what now?

Acknowledgements

Richard Adams
Philippa Scott
Keith Shackleton
Jacqueline Shackleton
Pete Wilkinson
Cassandra Phillips
Peter Hirst-Smith
The Green Magazine
WWF News International
The late Sir Peter Scott
Thorsons Publishing Group Ltd
The Royal Society for the Protection of Birds
Barry Fantoni
Clive Holloway
Time Magazine
ICM
Kate Jaspers (whale illustrations)
James Grant Management
GMP Public Relations
Jonathan Harper-Hill
Lorna Butland
The following have given permission to reproduce photographs in this book:
Peter Hirst-Smith (front cover; 4; 5; 7; 8; 10; 25; 32; 33; 34; 35; 37; 52; 55 both; 57; 58; 60; 61; 75; 77; 78)
Keith Shackleton (19; 26; 31; 40; 41)
Jacqueline Shackleton (13; 14; 15; 17; 18; 21; 23; 24)
Greenpeace/Morgan (29; 42; 45; 48; 76)
Philippa Scott (60; 62; 63; 64; 66; 71)
International Fund for Animal Welfare (68; 72)